CW00865596

IN A WORLD WE LOVE

To my daughter, *Madeline*

May you create a world your happiness can echo through for the ages.

Love,
Mom

In a world we love

We conserve water for our ocean and wondrous sea life.

We walk to school while enjoying the breeze and the little things that count.

We switch off a light and open a window on a beautiful sunny day.

We help our forests by reducing the amount of paper we use each and every day.

We plant a tree or two, maybe even three because trees help our planet and can carry on a legacy.

We recycle to save our ecosystems
and all forms of wildlife.

We volunteer in our community to
help with anything in need.

We remember to practice reusing and reducing.

We keep our planet green and clean.

We treat one another with kindness.

In a world I love....

My promise is to do my part to take care of planet Earth.

What is your promise to earth?

Alice Perez is a primary school teacher, writer, and best selling author. Her works include *Vamos a Veracruz*, her latest published title, *In a World We Love*, as well as a few other unpublished titles. Perez is a Texas native, born and raised in Houston. She has always had a passion for storytelling and writing. Perez discovered that expressing her ideas in children's books has been a fulfilling and enriching experience for her and she's been grateful for the opportunity to do so. Over the years, she has picked up her own style of writing which focuses on detailing and informing readers which she believes is key to engagement and bringing the story to life. Perez wrote her first story at the early age of ten for a fourth grade class project, sparking a love for what she does now. Little did she know, this assignment would be the beginning of her own story. Alice attests that you can begin your dreams at a young age and as you develop and change over time, your passion will shine through for everyone to see.

ILLUSTRATOR

Yuliia Chirka is a talented young artist and has been drawing since childhood. Chirka began studying at an art school in Dnipro, Ukraine where she graduated with honors in 2007. Her drawings have taken part in various art competitions. She never thought she would one day create children's illustrations and is delighted to have worked on *In A World We Love* as her debut. Yuliia has worked as a lighting designer since 2017 and became interested in children's illustration in 2019. One day, Chirka decided to take part in a challenge of creating an illustration for a competition on a popular social media platform, where she had to draw every day. She then participated in another challenge, then another, and slowly her portfolio began to grow and accumulate more pieces. Yuliia fell in love with creating children's illustrations more and more. So much so, that she took a course in creating casual graphics for games. She currently works as an 2-D Artist in one of the leading Ukrainian game studios.

Lightning Source UK Ltd.
Milton Keynes UK
UKHW051158260123
415918UK00009B/33

* 9 7 9 8 2 1 8 0 9 1 6 5 1 *